D1411631

WHAT IT MEANS TO BE
SERIES

PUBLISHER	Joseph R. DeVarennes
PUBLICATION DIRECTOR	Kenneth H. Pearson
ADVISORS	Roger Aubin
	Robert Furlonger
EDITORIAL MANAGER	Jocelyn Smyth
EDITORS	Ann Martin
	Shelley McGuinness
	Robin Rivers
	Mayta Tannenbaum
ARTISTS	Summer Morse
	Barbara Pileggi
	Steve Pileggi
	Mike Stearns
PRODUCTION MANAGER	Ernest Homewood
PRODUCTION ASSISTANTS	Catherine Gordon
	Kathy Kishimoto
PUBLICATION ADMINISTRATOR	Anna Good

Canadian Cataloguing in Publication Data

Langdon, Anne
  What it means to be—independent

(What it means to be; 11)
ISBN 0-7172-2235-7

1. Self-reliance — Juvenile literature.
2. Autonomy (Psychology) — Moral and ethical aspects — Juvenile literature.
I. Pileggi, Steve.   II. Title.   III. Title: Independent.   IV. Series.

BJ1533.S27L36 1987   j179'.9   C87-095053-3

WHAT IT MEANS TO BE . . .

INDEPENDENT

Written by
Anne Langdon

Illustrated by
Steve Pileggi

Independent people do many things on their own.

Hannah went shopping with her mother one morning. They bought a book called *101 Magic Tricks*. When they arrived home, there was still lots of time before kindergarten began.

"What can I do?" Hannah asked.

"Why don't you look at your new book?" suggested her mother.

Hannah was just learning how to read so the pictures showing the different tricks were a big help. She practiced one trick. Pretty soon she could make a pencil look as if it were sticking to her hand—all by itself!

"I did it! I did it!" she exclaimed.

Her mother gasped when she saw Hannah perform the trick.

"Won't your friends be surprised when you show them this afternoon at school!"

Independent people can have fun and learn new things all by themselves.

Not always doing what everybody else does is a sign of independence.

Bobby got a new Frisbee and was tossing it around his front yard. He was hoping a friend would come by to play. Sure enough, Paul and Jason walked over to have a look at his new Frisbee.

"Let's go throw it around," Jason said.

Soon the boys were off to the park. Tammy and Colette were playing on the swings. They ran over to play Frisbee with the boys.

Just then, Bobby threw the Frisbee harder than he meant and it flew to the far side of the park. Paul ran after it but he didn't come back.

"Let's go through the woods to look at the new houses they're building," he shouted.

"Yeah!" Jason answered.

"Come on!" Bobby called to Colette and Tammy. Tammy wanted to go, but Colette didn't think it was a good idea.

"I don't think we should," she said. Bobby laughed and ran off with Jason and Paul.

Tammy glared at Colette. "Why can't we go?" she asked as she stamped her foot.

"Mom and Dad told us never to go into the woods by ourselves," Colette explained.

"But we won't be by ourselves," Tammy replied. "The other kids will be with us."

"But they're not grownups," Colette said.

Tammy looked disappointed and cross. Colette had done the right thing, but she didn't know how to make Tammy understand.

"Let's ask Mom and Dad to take us to see the new houses when we go for our Sunday walk," she suggested.

Colette and Tammy took a long walk with their parents every Sunday afternoon before dinner. It was their way of exploring the neighborhood.

"Great idea!" Tammy said. It was something for her to look forward to without breaking any rules.

Sometimes your friends may do something that you know you shouldn't do. It's important to do what seems right to you.

Independent people look after their belongings.

Bobby was sitting on the front porch after dinner listening to his tape player. Ryan came by on his bike.

"Hey, is that the new Michael Jackson tape?" asked Ryan.

"Yeah. It's great," replied Bobby, snapping his fingers. "Come on up and listen."

Ryan parked his bike and sat by his friend. "I sure wish I could sing like Michael Jackson."

After the two boys listened to both sides of the tape, Ryan said, "Do you want to go for a bike ride?"

"Okay. I just have to put away my tape player first," replied Bobby.

"Your mom can do that for you," Ryan said, jumping on his bike. "Come on. I'll race you to the corner."

"No, Ryan. I have to put my things away. They belong to me," explained Bobby.

"Okay. I'll wait for you," said Ryan.

It is up to you to look after your things—no one else should do that for you.

Being independent means keeping your things in their proper places.

Paul, Kim, Ryan and Dylan were lying on the grass in Paul's front yard staring up at the clouds.

"And that cloud looks like a dinosaur," said Kim, squinting her eyes.

"Hey, look over there. See the big gray one spouting water like a whale?" laughed Ryan.

"I'm tired of doing this. Let's play ball," suggested Paul.

"Okay," said Dylan. "Let's go to the park."

"I'll go get my bat and ball," offered Paul as he ran off to the garage.

He knew his equipment was somewhere. He just wasn't sure where it was. He looked on the shelf where it should have been. He tried beside his dad's workbench. He even looked under his mom's car. Nothing!

Meanwhile his friends had gotten tired of waiting. They walked over to Dylan's house. Dylan knew exactly where his bat and ball and some extra gloves were kept. Soon he and Kim and Ryan were down at the park playing ball.

Finally, Paul found his bat behind the lawn mower and his ball under the garbage can lid. He trotted out to the front yard to show his friends, but they were gone. He ran all the way to the park. They were already playing baseball.

"What took you so long?" asked Ryan.

"Where did you get the baseball stuff?" Paul asked in surprise.

"From Dylan," answered Kim as she threw the ball to Ryan.

"Yeah, he found it right away," Ryan added.

Paul looked down at the bat and ball in his hands. He felt disappointed. Next time he would put his equipment where he could find it quickly and easily.

Putting things where they belong helps you to find them whenever you need them. When you put things where they belong without being told, it shows that you are independent.

If you are independent, you can have fun by yourself.

It was a long, slow Sunday. Jason had run out of things to do. All his friends were busy. He had no one to play with and he felt as if he would never have fun again.

Then he remembered his Batman costume, the one he had worn for Hallowe'en one year. It didn't take him long to put it on, but there was still no one to play with. He decided to wait for Janice to get up from her nap. He finally heard her thumping around in her room. He burst in to tell her that he was going to be Batman and she could be Robin.

Yawning, Janice said, "I don't want to be Robin. I want to fingerpaint."

Jason couldn't believe it. How could anyone not want to play Batman and Robin?! He stormed downstairs to complain to his mother.

"What's the problem?" she asked.

"I don't have anyone to play with," he moaned.

"Dinner won't be long. Why don't you go up to your room and see if you can amuse yourself?"

Slowly Jason trudged back to his room. He looked around to see if there was anything he could use. Suddenly he spied his table. It would be perfect! He turned it upside down. Then he slid between the legs, grabbed the tops of two of them and turned it into a Batmobile.

After a while, he flipped it over, unfolded a blanket and draped it over part of the bed and the table. The space in between was dark and cozy. He crawled inside. "This is the best Batcave I've ever made!" he thought.

He was busy thinking about the best way to make a Batcopter when his mother called, "Jason, dinner!"

"What are we having?" he asked as he trotted into the kitchen.

His mother looked at him and said, "Roast bat." Jason and Janice started laughing.

"I think you mean roast *beef,*" said Janice.

When she realized what she'd said, their mother began to laugh too.

If you use your imagination, you will find many fun activities to do alone.

Being independent means knowing how to act on instructions.

Paul and his father climbed in the car one Friday evening. They were on their way to buy Paul a globe that lit up so all the countries of the world glowed. While they were pulling out of the driveway, Paul saw Ryan and Bobby.

"Can I ask Ryan and Bobby to come?" Paul asked his father. "I promise we'll behave."

"Sure," his father said.

Paul called to his friends who ran to ask their parents and then jumped in the car.

"I'm going to get this real neat lamp," Paul told them. "It's a world that lights up!"

"Wow!" Ryan cried.

"A whole world just for you!" Bobby said with wonder. "You're lucky."

When they arrived at the store, Paul's father took them to the toy department. While he had them all together, he did something very smart. He told them to stay near him, but he also told them what to do in case one of them got lost.

"If you can't find the rest of us, go to the nearest cash register and tell the person working there that you're lost," he said.

Ryan was going to ask a question, but a large robot on wheels caught his attention. He was itching to see how it worked, so he headed toward it. It wasn't far away, and he could still see and hear Paul and his father.

Then way across the room, he saw a scuba diving display. He decided he would take a closer look.

"Can I help you with something?" he heard a voice ask as he examined the mannequin wearing scuba gear.

"Um, no," Ryan answered, "I'm just looking at this while my friend is buying something."

As he was talking, he looked around trying to find Paul and his dad and Bobby. He couldn't see them. He tried to find the man who had just spoken to him, but he was gone too! Then he remembered what he'd been told. He looked for a cash register. He found one and walked up to the woman working there.

"I can't find my friends," he said quietly.

"That's okay," she said with a big smile. "Come here and wait with me. Now, what's your name?"

After talking with him for a few moments, she picked up a microphone and made an announcement. A minute or two later, Paul and his father and Bobby came to get him. Ryan was very glad he'd paid attention and remembered the instructions Paul's father had given them.

If something unexpected happens while you're by yourself, it's especially important to stay calm and follow any directions you have been given.

Choosing your clothes and dressing yourself is a sign of independence.

Easter morning Tammy and Colette scampered around the house looking for the treats the Easter bunny had left for them. Their parents said they could have a few candies after breakfast, but the rest were for after dinner.

A special guest was coming to dinner—someone Tammy and Colette really looked forward to seeing. Their grandfather was coming, and he was going to sleep over too!

While their mother and father were getting everything ready for dinner, their father said, "I want you girls to look your best tonight."

"I know what I'm going to wear!" Colette said happily. "I'm going to lay it all out now." And she ran up the stairs, two at a time.

Tammy was going to dash off to her room too, but then she remembered that she had never dressed herself for a special occasion.

"Would you like some help?" her mother asked.

Tammy thought for a bit then asked, "Can I wear my dress with the hearts on it?"

"I don't see any reason why not," her mother answered.

"And can I wear my ballerina tights?"

Tammy's mother knew that she meant the white lace tights that she wore for special events. "Sure you can," she replied.

"And what about my black shiny shoes?"

"Looks to me as if you've got this all figured out," her mother said.

Tammy was very pleased. She had decided all by herself what to wear! A little while later, Tammy skipped down the stairs in her special Easter outfit. She was holding her brush and a ribbon.

"I've done everything by myself except for one thing. I need you to do my ponytail," she said to her father as she handed him the brush and ribbon.

"Glad to help out!" her father said, as he tied the ribbon in her hair.

Selecting clothes and getting dressed by yourself is easy with a little practice. It can be fun too.

If you are independent, you keep your bedroom tidy.

Hannah and Janice were playing up in Hannah's room. After a while Hannah's father came up to tell them to get ready for dinner.

"Look at this room!" he exclaimed. "You better clean it up!"

Looking around her, Janice saw what Hannah's father meant. "Why are you so messy?"

"It doesn't bother *me*," Hannah answered.

"Okay then," Janice said, "where are your pencil crayons?"

"Um," Hannah mumbled looking all over, "they're here somewhere."

Finally Janice said with a laugh, "No, they're not, they're at my place. You said I could borrow them."

"Oh," Hannah said grinning. "I see what you mean!"

By keeping your room neat you will be able to find things more easily and enjoy playing there more. It shows that you are responsible and that you respect your surroundings.

Independent people are willing to work hard now to achieve their future goals.

"The Green Sox won! The Green Sox won!" all the first graders were yelling in the schoolyard one morning. They continued cheering even when they were sitting at their desks.

"Could we keep it down to a dull roar?" Ms. Barclay asked.

"But the Green Sox won!" Dylan exclaimed. "Our favorite baseball team won!"

"Yes, I know—everybody's talking about it," she replied.

"I'm going to be the world's best baseball player when I grow up," Paul bragged.

"No, I am!" Ryan cried.

"Too bad for you two, but I'm going to be the *best* player on the *best* team," Dylan said finally.

"One thing you should all keep in mind," their teacher said, "is that all the great players began practicing when they were your age. It takes a long time and a lot of hard work to become the best."

When the grade one class was let out for recess, each boy jumped up and down trying to convince the others that he was the one to watch. The teacher's words stuck in Dylan's mind. It seemed silly to stand around talking. He figured it would be better to practice, just as she had mentioned.

"Why don't we play some ball?" he asked.

"Yeah, after school!" Bobby said.

"In fact," Dylan said, thinking about it a bit more, "why don't we see if we can have a baseball team of our own?" All the other boys thought that was a wonderful idea, but no one was sure how to go about it.

"Let's ask someone," Dylan suggested. "After all, we don't need much: some bats, balls and gloves. We've got plenty of places to play."

Thinking about it later, Dylan realized how easy it would be to arrange regular practices. Then he thought about all the fun they could have. And finally, he thought how thrilling it would be to be on a real professional team one day.

A few days later, Dylan joined his friends after school. His arms were loaded with baseball equipment.

"Hey, what's all that for?" Paul asked.

"Don't you remember?" Dylan asked, looking at his friends. "We were going to set up our own team."

"Oh yeah," they said. "We forgot."

"Well, I didn't," Dylan replied.

"Is it all yours?" Ryan asked.

"Nope," Dylan said. "I asked Ms. Barclay if there was anything we could use. She said we could borrow this school equipment as long as we promised to put it all back afterwards. Plus, she made me promise one other thing."

"What?" the other boys wanted to know.

With a grin, Dylan answered, "She made me promise that I'd give her my autograph when I became a famous baseball player!"

It may take a long time to reach some of your goals, but if you can think and act independently you will keep working towards them.

Even independent people need others.

Eva had lots of friends to play with on school days. But since she was new to the neighborhood, not many kids visited her on the weekends. Eva was good at thinking up things to do by herself.

She was in the middle of a hopscotch game one day when Jason came by on his skateboard.

"Hi Eva!" he called out to her. "What are you doing?"

"Oh, just playing hopscotch," Eva answered.

"I've never done that before," he admitted. "Why don't we switch? You can try my skateboard and I'll play hopscotch."

Eva hopped on his skateboard and almost fell off while Jason tried to figure out her hopscotch game. Looking at one another doing something new, they had to laugh.

"Tell you what," Jason said, "you teach me how to do this and I'll give you a few tips on skateboarding."

Even though you can have fun by yourself, it's also nice to learn something new from other people.

If you are independent, you finish jobs on time.

The end of the school year was coming up. While the grade one children sat in their classroom those last few days, many of them stared out the windows longing to be out in the warm sunshine.

"We're going to have a year-end party," Ms. Barclay announced, "here in our classroom the last afternoon of the year. Your parents will be invited. Miss Norman, our student teacher, is going to help us get ready."

"We should make invitations for you to take home," Miss Norman said. "Who has any ideas?"

"I do!" Joey cried. "I could do something on my computer."

"That's a good idea," she approved. The class agreed.

"We'll have to do this quickly though," she said, "because the party is soon."

First the class decided what the invitation should say. Then they decided how it should look. Finally, they came up with a design that Joey thought he could do on his computer.

He ran home after school to tell his mother about the project. "My teacher says I need to do it fast."

"Are you going to start tonight?" his mother asked.

"No, Ryan and I have to finish a project," Joey said. "I'll do it tomorrow."

The next day after school Joey started the invitation. His mother helped with the typing. Together, they had a lot of fun. The task was finished quicker than he expected. Joey was very pleased with how the invitation turned out. He rushed to school the following day to show the class.

"Thank you for helping to get our party off to such a good start!" Miss Norman said to Joey.

Independent people know how to schedule their time so that they can live up to their commitments. If you are independent, you can work and play by yourself. Here are a few ways to be more independent:
- Work happily on your own.
- Think for yourself.
- Keep your room tidy.
- Finish tasks on time.
- Work toward your goals.

Printed and bound in U.S.A.